Shhh...Mommy has a Migraine

written by Penny Teague
Illustrated by Abid Rozdar

ISBN: 978-1-954341-75-3 (Paperback)
        978-1-954341-78-4 (Ebook)

The views expressed in this book are solely those of the author and do not necessarily reflect the views of the publisher, and the publisher hereby disclaims any responsibility for them.

Writers' Branding
1800-608-6550
www.writersbranding.com
orders@writersbranding.com

To my children
Kayle, Amber, and Erin

Good morning little one,
Mommy loves you.
Let's go and play today!

We'll have breakfast and a cuddle.

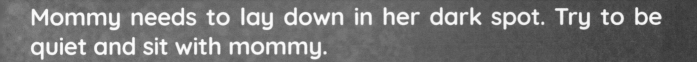

Mommy needs to lay down in her dark spot. Try to be quiet and sit with mommy.

Oh little one you brought mommy an ice pack and a cold drink.

Mommy gets up and makes you some lunch.

Look sissy is home!!

Sissy takes you outside.
You and Sissy talk about mommy.
Mommy has another migraine.
Poor mommy.
You didn't do it she says migraines just
come on and get her.

You sneak in and check on mommy when sissy is cooking
dinner.

Mommy smiles and you curl up next to her. Mommy falls back asleep with you sitting there.

You see your kitty laying on the bed with mommy you lean over and give her kisses you know she is there to help mommy too.

You see headlights you know Daddy is home! You slip out of mommy & daddy's room. The door opens and daddy sees you. He knows right away that mommy is laying down with a migraine. Daddy picks you up and gives you a big hug. He tells you that he loves you and is going to check on mommy.

He sends you back to help sissy.

You watch daddy go into mommy's dark spot. You see him kiss mommy on the forehead and hand her a drink and some medicine.

Mommy takes her medicine like a good mommy. Daddy smiles and tells her he loves her and he leaves her dark spot.

addy comes out and sits on the couch
ith you.

You cuddle up next to him and ask him ho
mommy is. You ask him how come momn
has migraines. You ask if you made it come. H
kisses you on the forehead like he did momm

He tells you it's not your fault and that momn
is going to be better now that she has had
nap and her medicine.

Daddy starts reading you a story. Suddenly you hear mommy's door open!!

You see lights on in the room. That is always a good sign! Mommy is up and hopefully feeling alright.

Daddy smiles and asks how she i
Mommy say
"I'm all right for now

You all sit down for dinne

fter dinner mommy cuddles with
ou in your bed.

he tells you that she loves you
nd thank you for your help.

Together you read a book for bed and she sits with you until you fall asleep.

Mommy gets up and kisses you on the forehead and says,

"Good night little one, Mommy loves you."

CPSIA information can be obtained
at www.ICGtesting.com
Printed in the USA
BVHW021708151121
621680BV00002B/27